duck duck

Draw a line to the matching ducks.

Ducks have webbed feet.

Can you draw what comes next?

Trace the word then write.

lion lion

Lions roar very loudly!

How many lion cubs can you count?

Draw a lion.

Trace the word.

giraffe *giraffe*

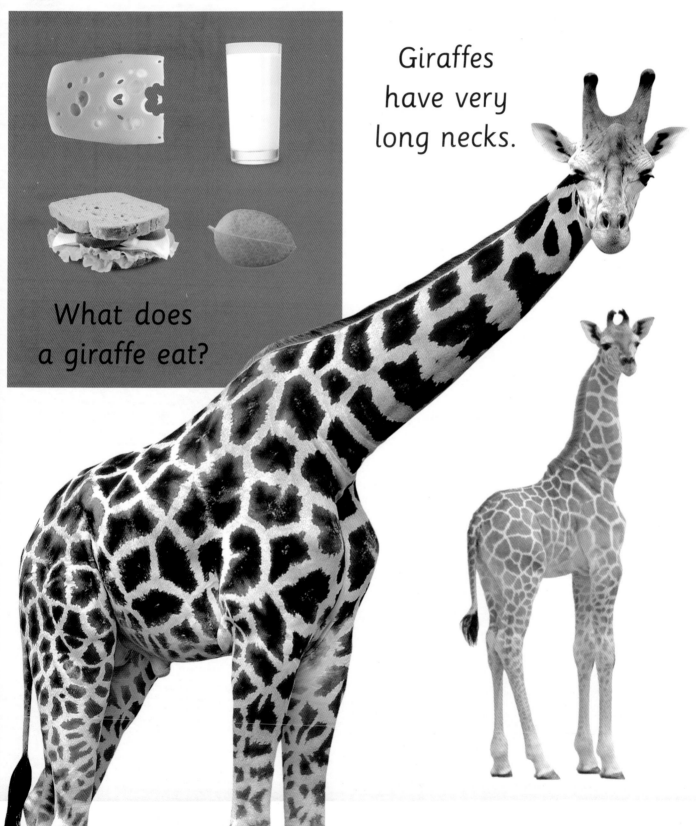

Giraffes
have very
long necks.

What does
a giraffe eat?

Trace the word then write.

pig pig

Draw a pig.

Pigs love mud.

Help the piglet find the apple through the maze.

Trace the word then write.

horse horse

Count the horseshoes.

Draw a horse.

Horses can run very fast.

Trace the word then write.

cat cat

Circle the orange cats.

Finish drawing the cat.

Cats lick their fur to keep clean.

Trace the word then write.

bird bird

Birds hatch from eggs.

Count the eggs.

Draw a bird.

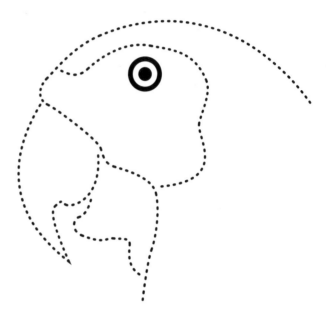

Birds have wings.

Follow the bird flying in the sky.

Trace the word then write.

fish fish

Circle the spotted fish.

Connect a line to
the striped fish.

Trace the bubbles.

10 1
9

7

8

5

6

4

3 2

Draw the fish.

Fish
have
fins.

Trace the word then write.

dog *dog*

Dogs love to **play.**

Draw a dog.

kennel

cage

aquarium

bed

Where do dogs live?

tiger *tiger*

Draw a tiger.

Tigers are large **cats.** They have **stripes.**

Circle the tigers.

Trace the word.

elephant *elephant*

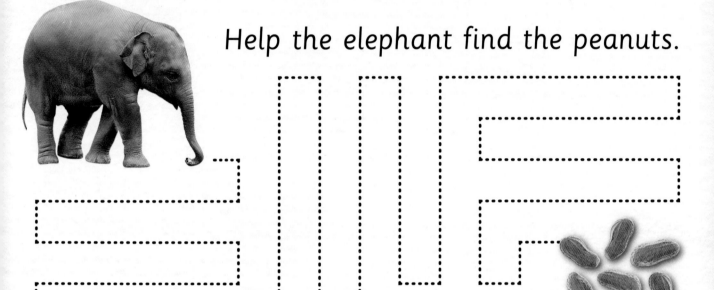

Help the elephant find the peanuts.

Elephants
have long **trunks**
and large **ears.**

frog frog

Baby frogs are called tadpoles.

Circle the green frogs.

Follow the bouncing frogs by tracing the dotted line.